The Noctuary of Narcissus Batt

by the same author

for adults
New Weather
Mules
Why Brownlee Left
Quoof
Selected Poems 1968–1983
Meeting the British
Madoc
Shining Brow
The Annals of Chile
New Selected Poems 1968–1994
The Faber Book of Contemporary Irish Poetry (editor)

for children
The Last Thesaurus (with illustrations by Rodney Rigby)

The Noctuary of Narcissus Batt

Paul Muldoon

illustrated by Markéta Prachatická

faber and faber
LONDON · BOSTON

First published in 1997
by Faber and Faber Limited
3 Queen Square London WC1N 3AU

Typeset by Faber and Faber Ltd
Printed in England by Clays Ltd, St Ives plc

A CIP record for this book
is available from the British Library

ISBN 0–571–19020–0

10 9 8 7 6 5 4 3 2 1

for Augusta and Miranda

The Noctuary of Narcissus Batt

A November night. Late. A lump of peat
falling softly in the fire
sends an echo through Purdysburn, the seat
of Narcissus Batt, Esquire.

A falling turf, a falling log or coal
gives a tap, at most a slap:
Narcissus is such a sensitive soul
it sounds like a thunderclap.

So that he jumps up out of the wingchair
as if out of his own skin
which has itself suffered such wear and tear
it's now almost paper-thin.

It's on this unlikely sheet of vellum
that he jots down as they pass
such night-notes as, 'When I start at a flame
I feel such a silly ass.'

At which an ASS roars from the chimney-breast:
'When Our Lord rode upon it
the ass was *silly* in the sense of "blessed".
That's the bee in *my* bonnet.'

A BEE blusters out of the velvet drapes
into this psycho-drama:
'I like to think, despite my convict's stripes,
that I'm the cat's pyjamas.'

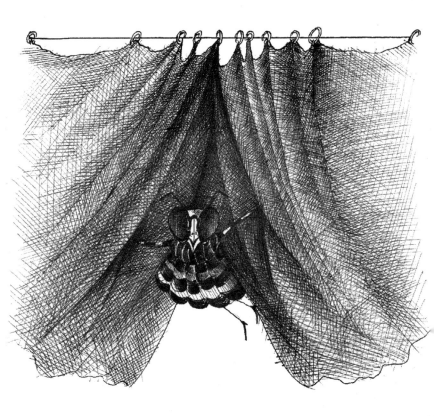

A CAT pats its waistcoat of watered silk:
'Although I run the danger
of seeming so, since I won't share my milk,
I'm no dog in the manger.'

'The time will come,' a DOG begins to girn,
'when money will be so scant
that a great mansion such as Purdysburn
will be a white elephant.'

'Don't forget,' an ELEPHANT flicks his ash,
'such ideas are put about
by all sorts of riffraff and scum and trash
who must be ferreted out.'

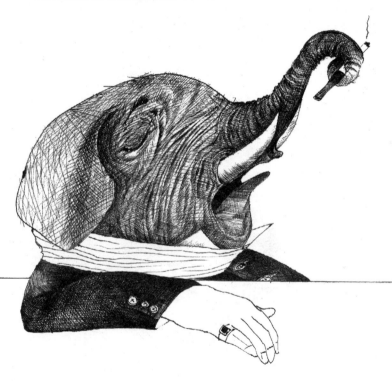

'As for my "habit",' a FERRET whistles,
'of going "straight for the throat"
of rabbits, that I'm lumped in with weasels
and stoats really gets my goat.'

A GOAT butts in, as goats are wont to do:
'This talk of violence evokes
memories of the front at Waterloo
where howitzers wreaked havoc.'

As a HAWK or *heafoc*, at one fell swoop,
whips the cloth off the table:
'The chicken from the modern chicken-coop
is quite impalatable.'

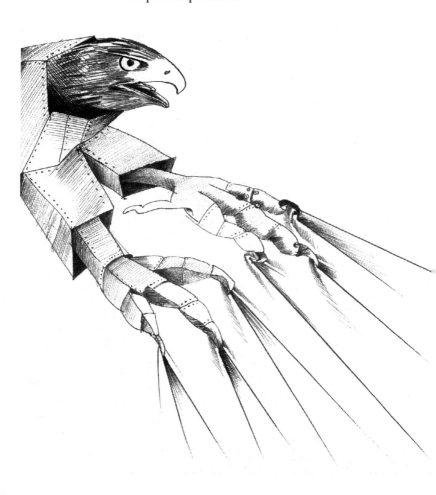

'One day,' an IMPALA moans, 'I'll shake off
my invisible shackles;
until then I'll kick out with my hind hooves
at that huge pack of jackals.'

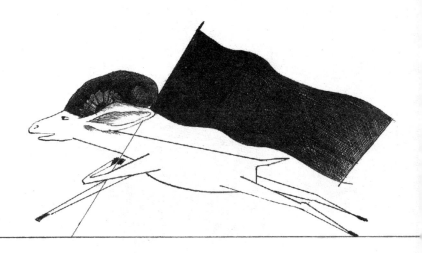

'Just because I've got a little blood-stain,'
a JACKAL sneers, 'on my shirt,
doesn't mean I should be dragged yet again
before some kangaroo-court.'

'I jump for joy, I jump because I'm glad,'
a KANGAROO now hazards,
'not because I'm a bounder or a cad
or some sort of lounge-lizard.'

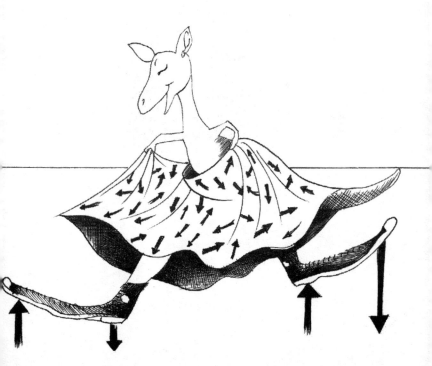

'So you imagine,' a LIZARD seems stunned,
'that in this great carbuncle
on my brow there's a semi-precious stone?
I'll be a monkey's uncle.'

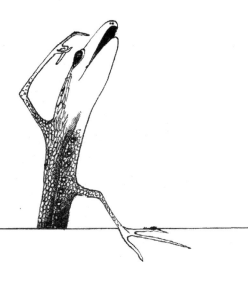

'That Charles Darwin,' a MONKEY dryly coughs,
'it's just another tall tale
from him. It's time for me to blow his gaff,
to sing like a nightingale.'

'Would that I might,' a NIGHTINGALE entreats,
'clasp Johnny to my bosom . . .'
(From which some may take it she means John Keats
and not Sir John O'Possum.)

'I'll have you know I'm not some absentee
landlord from County Cavan,'
an OPOSSUM grunts, 'though I seem to be
in what they term "pig heaven".'

A PIG flies in: 'Neither cast ye your swine
before pearls nor praise with faint
damns when, your honour (if I may opine),
your dust will soon turn to quaint.'

'Quaint? *Quaint?* A QUINNAT salmon, or
  'Chinook',
now leaps to its own defence:
'After these "humans" catch us on a hook,
they give us a "rabbit-punch".'

'Nothing compares to the high-rise warren,'
a RABBIT ponders some bark,
'where our barren lives are made more barren
by dope-dealers and loan-sharks.'

A SHARK slides past: 'If you know in your gut
that the issues are murky –
never cleanly-drawn, never clearly-cut –
we *might* be talking turkey.'

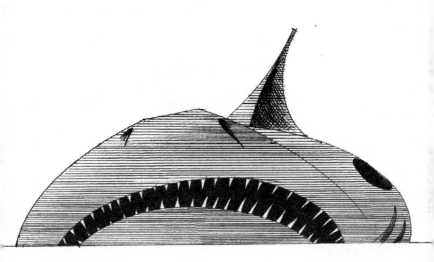

'This time of year,' a TURKEY swanks, 'I find
I've much too much on my plate.
The whole thing's such a bind and such a grind
that I ulu . . . ululate.'

An ULULA, or owl: 'Who gives a hoot
about Van Dyke and Voltaire
and Vermeer and Virgil and those old coots,
except for culture-vultures?'

'I'm just,' a VULTURE flabbers in, 'I'm just
back from the scene of a crime
where a few of us sated our blood-lust
and had a whale of a time.'

'I'm equipped with sonar,' snortles a WHALE,
'for detecting limpet-mines
covered with interlocking plates and scales
like twelve-banded xenurines.'

'Not since Hernan Cortez or Cabeza
"The Heifer-Head" de Vaca,'
a XENURINE sniffs, 'have we kabassous
endured such yakkety-yak.'

'A patron of the arts, what would Batt say,'
a YAK looks up from grazing,
'if he knew that paintings would one day
look much like zebra-crossings?'

'To use such a phrase,' a ZEBRA tut-tuts,
'of a cross-walk's two-tone lines
is not merely literal-minded but
positively asinine.'

Just as an ASS's head begins to flesh
itself out from the mantel
Narcissus jumps up and, quick as a flash,
wraps himself in his mantle.

He flaps one wing as if it were a page
on which the ink is still wet.
His wing is blue-black and blotted and botched.
His heart is a paperweight.

A falling turf, a green stick full of sap,
sends up a blue-yellow roil
as he rubs himself down with saddle-soap
and a touch of neat's-foot oil.

Narcissus Batt wedges himself between
Balzac and Sir Thomas Browne
and turns in for the day, a day that leans
heavily towards the town.